Key Stage 3

Workbook Levels 6–8

EDUCATIONAL

Name: Maria Sobota

Class:

Science

Richard Barnett
Marilyn Brodie
Derek Green
Terry Hudson

First published 1999

Letts Educational
9–15 Aldine Street
London W12 8AW
Tel 0181 740 2270
Fax 0181 740 2280

Design and page layout: Ken Vail Graphic Design, Cambridge

Illustrations: Ken Vail Graphic Design

British Library Cataloguing-in-Publication Data

A CIP record for this book is available from the British Library

ISBN 1 84085 223 2

Printed and Bound

Letts Educational is the trading name of
BPP (Letts Educational) Ltd

Contents

Contents

Physical Processes

Introduction

This **Class Activity and Homework Book** has been written to help you as you study science at Key Stage 3. It is part of a range of books and booklets produced by Letts to help you to prepare for the end of Key Stage tests and to encourage you to enjoy your science. The other resources in the series are:

- *Key Stage 3 Science Classbook*
- *Key Stage 3 Science Workbook Levels 3–5*
- *Key Stage 3 Experimental and Investigative Skills*

The Science Classbook contains all of the science content of the National Curriculum that you will need to know. The other books are designed to link with it and make you think about your science even more.

This particular book covers the National Curriculum from level 6 to level 8. Each activity has a note telling you the level you have been working at. This is so you can keep a record of your progress and so you can aim to reach higher and higher levels. The topics follow the pattern in the Classbook and direct links to pages are given in a box at the end of the first page of each activity.

This book is made so that you can write onto it directly. This will keep all of your work in one place and help you to organise it. This is vital when it comes to preparing for tests. Also, it will allow you to spend more time thinking and learning your science, and less time copying important notes and diagrams. Use the space wisely and think hard about what you need to write down. Short, clear answers will be better to study from later.

We hope that you will find the activities useful and interesting. Within the book there are many different types of tasks, so that you are not always doing the same thing. You will find questions to answer, data to sort out, problems to solve, puzzles to complete and diagrams to discuss and explain. Sometimes you will be working on your own and sometimes your teacher will ask you to work with others to discuss ideas. Communicating science in this way is very important, but don't forget to use any spaces within the activity pages to keep notes.

Your teacher will tell you which activities to do and which homeworks to try. The homeworks often ask you to look around at home and think about science away from school. Remember to be careful and always follow any safety instructions and warnings.

Finally, we hope that this book, and the other books in the series, will help you to understand and enjoy your science.

1 The building blocks of life

A house is made of bricks and in the same way the bodies of animals and plants are made of cells.

Use the words below to label the diagrams (you may need to use some words more than once).

1

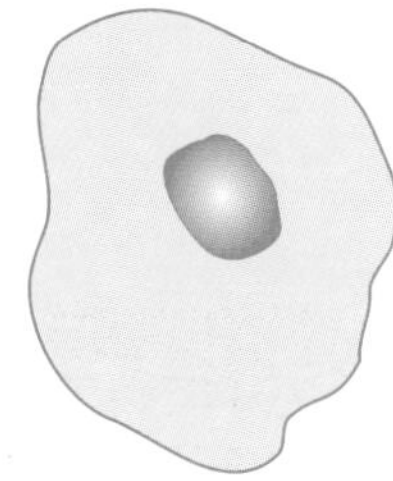

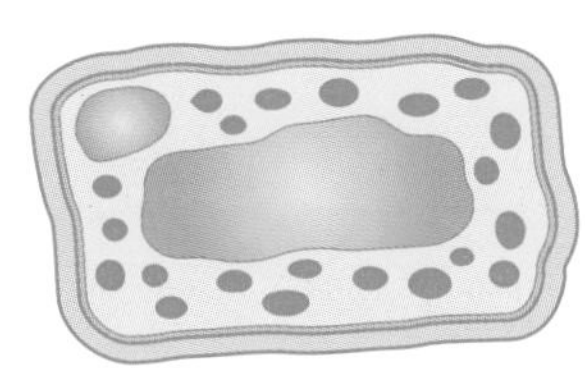

nucleus   cell membrane   vacuole   cell wall   cytoplasm   chloroplasts

2 Complete the table below by ticking the parts present in animal and plant cells.

3 In the third column write in the job each part does using the list below to help you:

	Animal cells	Plant cells	Jobs they do
cell membrane			
cell wall			
chloroplasts			
cytoplasm			
nucleus			
vacuole			

a control centre of the cell

b allows cells to use the Sun's energy

c is filled with watery fluid

d forms a thin, flexible outer skin

e where many of the chemical reactions take place in the cell

f is thick, rigid and made of cellulose.

National Curriculum links

- Life processes and living things
- Life processes and cell activity

If you can describe cell structure and explain the differences between plant and animal cells, you are working at level 6.

Links with the Classbook

Unit 2 *pages* 6–7

The diagram below shows a group of cells.

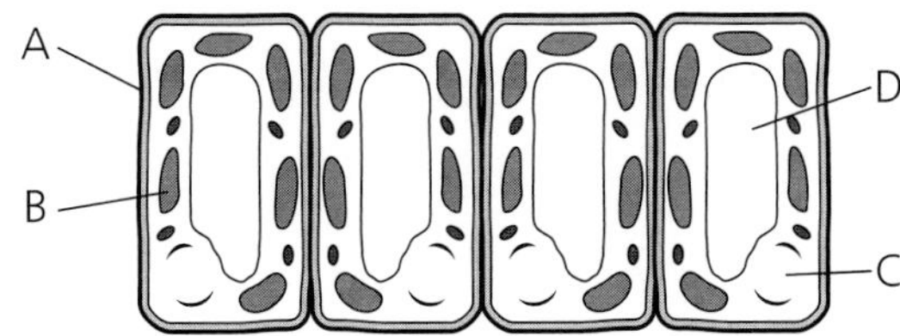

1 Name the structures labelled A, B, C and D.

A ....

B ....

C ....

D ....

2 Describe the main job carried out by the structures labelled A, B, C and D.

A ....

B ....

C ....

D ....

3 Are the cells from an animal or a plant?

....

4 Give **four** reasons to support your answer to question 3.

....

....

....

....

2 Blood and guts

What to do

You are going to build a model gut. Follow the instructions and then answer the questions at the bottom of the page.

Step 1: Take one piece of A4 paper and one piece of A3 paper.

Step 2: Measure the sides of each piece of paper and work out the area.

A4 paper	length = ... cm	width = ... cm		
	area = length × width	= .... cm^2		
A3 paper	length = ... cm	width = ... cm		
	area = length × width	= .... cm^2		

Step 3: Roll up the A4 paper so that it makes a tube. Roll it so that it is as long as possible.

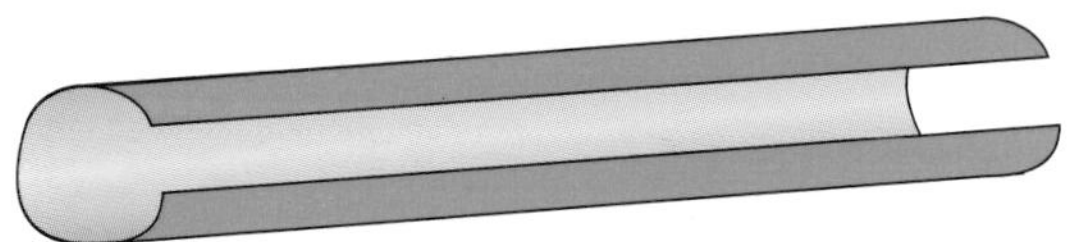

Step 4: Tape the tube closed. This is the outside wall of the gut.

Step 5: **Challenge!** You need to make a tube out of the A3 paper, but it must do the following things!

a it must fit inside the A4 tube with no parts sticking out
b you cannot cut the A3 tube
c the edges of the tube must not overlap.

(*Hint* – look at page 18 of your Classbook and see if it gives you inspiration.)

The A3 paper has become the inner wall of the gut.

1 What is the total surface area of the inner wall of your model gut? ....

2 Use the model to help explain how the structure of the gut helps small molecules of food to be absorbed. ....

National Curriculum links

- Life processes and living things
- Humans as organisms

If you can describe and explain how surface area relates to the absorption of food in the gut, you are working at level 6.

Links with the Classbook

Unit 8
pages 18–19

Respiration and photosynthesis 3

1 Write the word equation for respiration:

....

2 Write the word equation for photosynthesis:

....

In a piece of homework a pupil wrote:

Animals carry out respiration but plants carry out photosynthesis.

3 In the space provided explain why this is wrong. Write what the pupil should have written, especially about the processes carried out by plants.

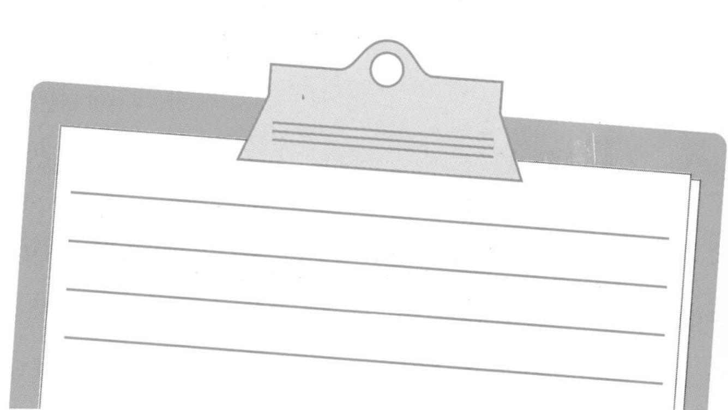

We know that plants need daylight to carry out photosynthesis. This means that at night they are only able to carry out respiration.

4 Do you think there might be a time when a plant produces exactly the same amount of carbon dioxide from respiration as it needs for photosynthesis?

....

5 What time of day do you think this might be and why?

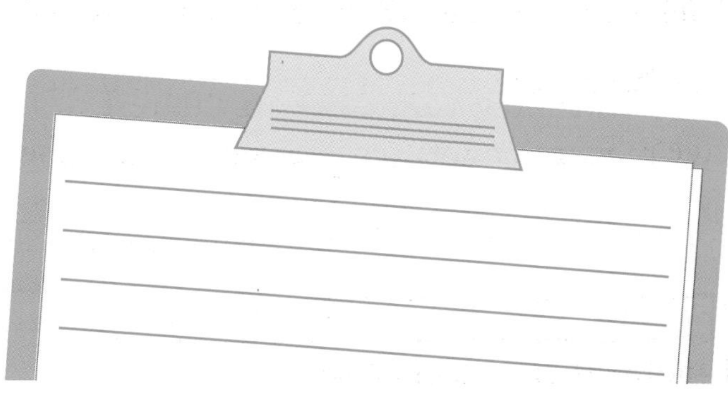

National Curriculum links

- Life processes and living things
- Humans as organisms and green plants as organisms
- Respiration and nutrition

If you can explain the processes of respiration and photosynthesis in terms of the main underlying chemical changes, you are working at level 7.

Links with the Classbook

Units 12 and 23
pages 26–27 and *pages* 48–49

4 Dying for a smoke

Cigarette smoke contains over 1000 different chemicals, many of which can damage your body.

These include:

- nicotine
- carbon monoxide
- tar
- irritants such as dust and ammonia
- heat.

This still does not stop young people from starting to smoke. They run the risk of serious illness later in life or even death from a disease such as cancer.

The ultimate commercial!

You are going to work in a small groups of three or four. Some groups will be A's and some will be B's. Your teacher will organise you.

Group A – You are going to plan a two minute anti-smoking commercial to be shown on television. You are going to show how harmful smoking can be.

Group B – You are going to plan a two minute pro-smoking commercial which will also be shown on television. You are going to show smoking as fashionable and pleasurable.

Remember, whichever campaign your commercial supports, you will be reaching millions of people and they need to be convinced of your arguments.

You will show your work to the rest of the class. You might want to write a script and act it out, produce a series of pictures or present your work in any other way you think is suitable.

National Curriculum links

- Life processes and living things
- Humans as organisms
- Breathing

If you can explain the biological changes resulting from smoking you are working at level 8.

Links with the Classbook

Unit 11
pages 24–25

Homework 4

Cigarette advertising is banned in many places. This is because smoking damages health and it is a bad idea to encourage people to smoke.

However, it is still possible to see tobacco advertising. Often it is not obvious that cigarettes are being advertised. It is important that people are aware of how they might be encouraged to smoke without realising it.

1 Find as many examples of this 'hidden' tobacco advertising as you can.

2 Try to explain how the advertisement is getting its message across and say who it might appeal to.

Type of advertising	What is the message?	Who might it appeal to?

3 Write down **three** good arguments against smoking.

a ....

b ....

c ....

5 Reproduction

Many cells in the body are specially adapted to do their jobs.

1 Label the diagrams below. Pages 8 and 9 of your Classbook will be helpful.

a

b

2 What is each cell called?

a .... b ....

3 How is each cell specially adapted to do its job?

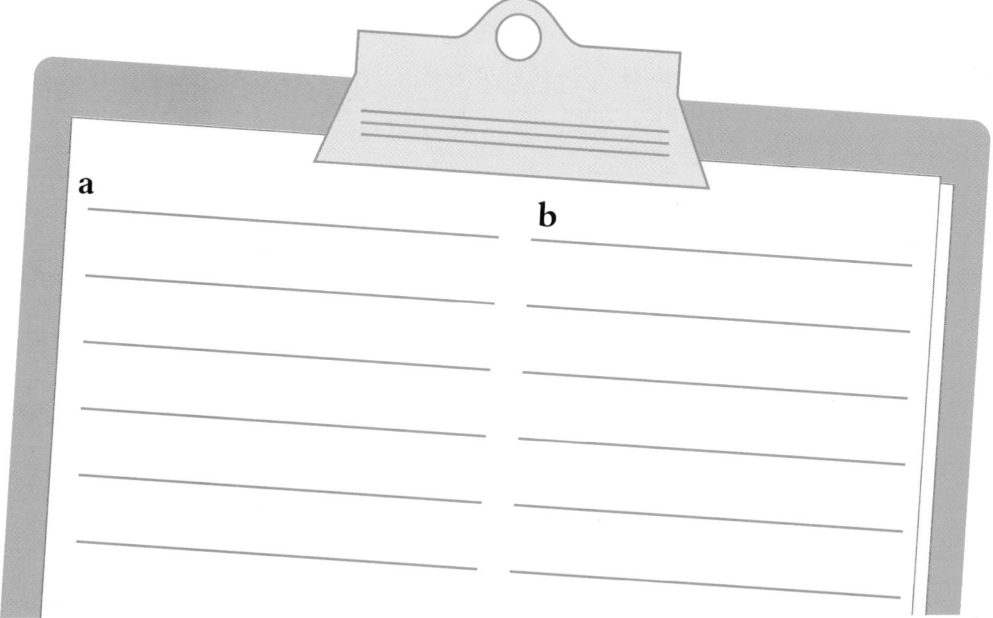

National Curriculum links

- Life processes and living things
- Humans as organisms

If you can explain how cells are adapted to their jobs you are working at level 7. If you can explain the importance of the menstrual cycle, and use technical terms, you are working at level 6.

Links with the Classbook

Unit 3 and Unit 17
pages 8–9 and *pages* 48–49

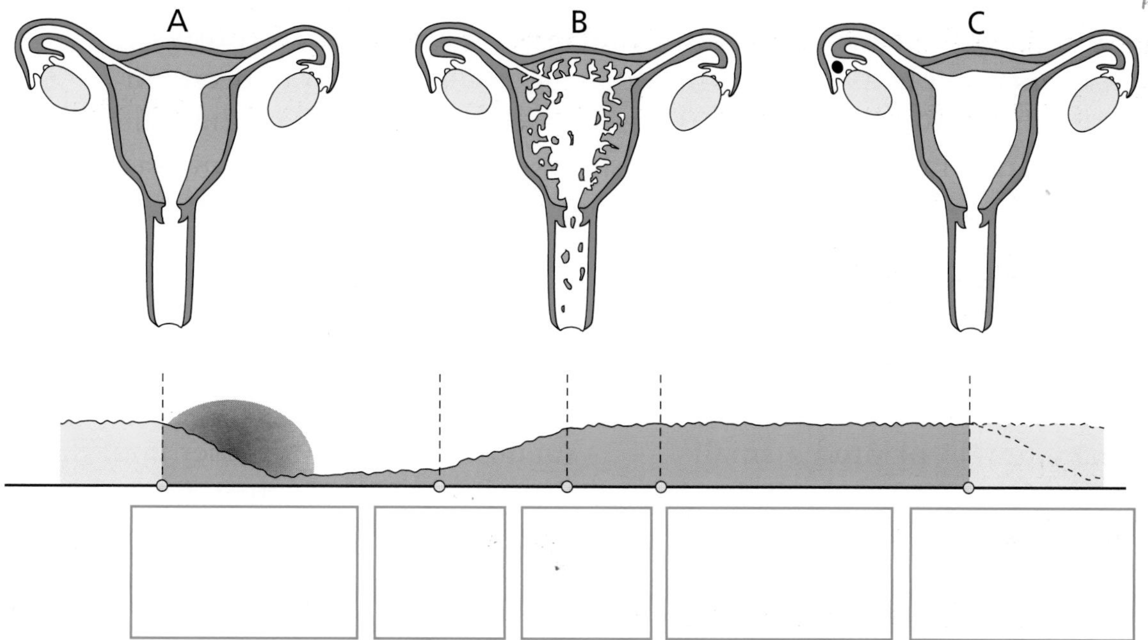

4 Use the diagrams above, and the information on page 37 of your Classbook, to label each stage of the menstrual cycle. Fill in the boxes on the diagram.

5 Place the top diagrams in the correct order.

1 = ...

2 = ...

3 = ...

6 In the space below describe why the menstrual cycle is so important.

....

....

....

....

....

....

6 Plants – the energy trap

You are going to make posters to show how two famous scientists did experiments on plants and got results which helped us to understand photosynthesis. Working with a partner, read through each of the following accounts. Then make a poster which shows how each experiment was carried out, what the results were and how these results can be explained.

Experiment 1

In the 17th century, a scientist called van Helmont did the following experiment. He planted a small willow tree in a pot of soil, having first weighed the soil and the willow separately. He then left the willow for five years, making sure that the soil was kept well watered. Five years later he dug up the willow and weighed it, and he also weighed the soil on its own again. These were his results:

Mass (kg)	Before planting	Five years later
Willow	2	77
Soil	100	100

Experiment 2

In the 18th century, Joseph Priestley carried out an experiment. He burnt a candle in a sealed chamber until the flame went out. He then divided the air from this chamber into two separate glass containers. In one container he placed a green plant; no plant was placed in the other container. Both containers were put in a sunny place. Ten days later he found a lighted candle would burn in the first container, but not in the second.

Main points of your plan

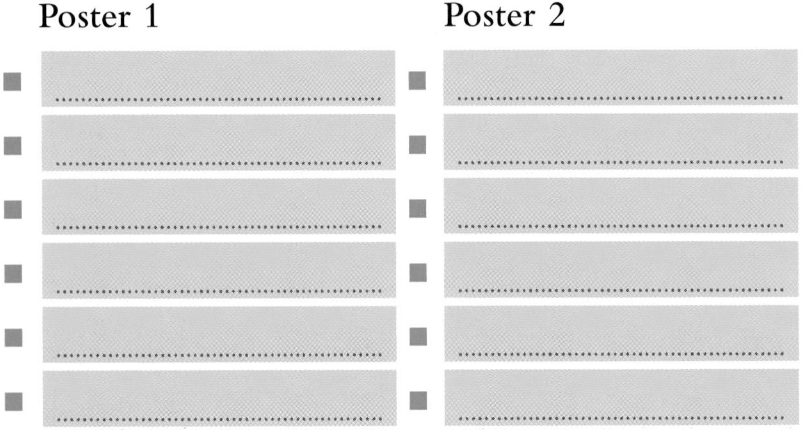

National Curriculum links

- *Life processes and living things*
- *Green plants as organisms*

If you can explain the processes of photosynthesis you are working at level 7.

Links with the Classbook

Unit 22 and 23
pages 46–49

Imagine that two friends were away from school when you were shown how to test a leaf for starch.

Prepare some instructions for your friends. Stress any safety precautions they should take when doing the test.

Your instructions can be in the form of a written account, flow diagram, pictures, a combination of these, or any other way you think is helpful.

Testing for starch

Safety Points

7 The causes of variety

The individuals that make up a particular species of plant or animal are all different. These differences can be caused by **environmental factors** or can be due to **inherited differences.**

What to do

Work in a pair or as a group. Read through the article below about environmental variation. Discuss and record answers to the questions.

Identical twins come from a single fertilised egg that divided in half before each half grew into a new baby. Because their genetic material is identical, you would expect them to be exactly the same in every way.

Studying identical twins that were separated at birth and brought up in different situations, can give us some idea of how important environment might be. If one twin has a healthy home life with good food and exercise and the other is less fortunate, there can be a visible difference in their adult size and shape.

Plants can also show how the environment can affect inherited characteristics. Identical plants are easy to create from cuttings. When they are grown in different areas, they can produce different yields, depending on sunshine, rainfall and soil fertility.

1 How are identical twins formed?

....

....

2 How has studying identical twins helped to show that environmental differences can cause variation?

....

....

3 Why is it easier to study environmental variation in plants rather than people?

....

....

National Curriculum links

- Life processes and living things
- Variation, classification and inheritance

If you can describe some of the factors that cause variation between living things you are working at level 6.

Links with the Classbook

Unit 28
pages 58–59

Homework 7

1 Find the following words in your Classbook (pages 58 and 59) and write a brief explanation for each.

Mutation

....

Dominant

....

Inherited characteristic

....

Environmental factors

....

Genes

....

2 If identical twins come from a single fertilised egg which divides as shown in figure 2 on page 59 of your Classbook, how do you think non-identical twins might be produced?

Use the space below to draw or write your explanation.

8 Life on Earth

1 Define the following words:

Habitat ....

Community ....

Ecosystem ....

2 Make a list of some of the ecosystems around your school. Show which ones are natural and which ones, like gardens, are artificial.

....

....

....

....

....

3 What is competition? ....

....

4 One way to avoid competition is to be a **nocturnal** or night-time animal. How are nocturnal animals adapted to life at night?

....

....

....

....

National Curriculum links

- Life processes and living things
- Living things in their environment
- Adaptation, feeding relationships and competition

If you can explain how relationships between organisms can affect population size, you are working at level 7–8.

Links with the Classbook

Units 32–36
pages 67–75

1 Choose a meal you eat often and particularly like. Construct **food chains** for all the ingredients but instead of just writing out the names, try to find pictures to illustrate your diagrams.

2 Draw a picture or diagram to show the effects of insecticides or other toxic substances on food chains and webs.

9 Food chains and food webs

Green plants can make their own food by using energy from the Sun in the process called **photosynthesis.** Some animals eat plants and are themselves eaten by other animals. This is called a **food chain.** In a particular habitat several food chains may overlap with each other to form a **food web.**

In the space below is part of a food web from a pond.

small fish

water snails

pond weed

What to do

1 Add the plants and animals from the list below, in the right places, to build up the food web for the pond. Information on pages 70 to 73 of your Classbook will help you.

waterside plants   heron   water fleas   water insects   microscopic plants   ducks

2 Draw arrows between the animals and plants to show what eats what.

3 Add **four** more plants and animals to make the web even larger.

National Curriculum links

- Life processes and living things
- Living things in their environment

If you are able to describe feeding relationships using food webs and construct pyramids of number you are working at level 7.

Links with the Classbook

Units 34–35
pages 70–73

4 Use page 70 of your Classbook to look up the terms, **producer**, **primary consumer** and **secondary consumer**. Write your definitions for each in the spaces below.

A producer is … ....

....

An example is … ....

A primary consumer is … ....

....

An example is … ....

A secondary consumer is … ....

....

An example is … ....

5 On the diagram of your pond food web underline all the producers in black.

6 On the diagram of your pond food web underline the primary consumers in blue.

7 On the diagram of your pond food web underline the secondary consumers in red.

8 Read the section from page 71 of the Classbook on pyramids of number. Select a food chain from the pond. In the space on the right draw the shape of the pyramid of numbers you would expect for the chain.

Every habitat has several food chains and some plants and animals may play a part in more than one chain. This complex set of relationships is called a **food web.** All the plants and animals in a food web are linked together. Removing just one can disrupt the whole web.

The diagram on the right shows a marine food web (this diagram is also found on page 72 of your Classbook). Write the name of each organism on a small piece of card, shuffle the pieces and put them face down on the table. If you are working in a group take turns to pick one up.

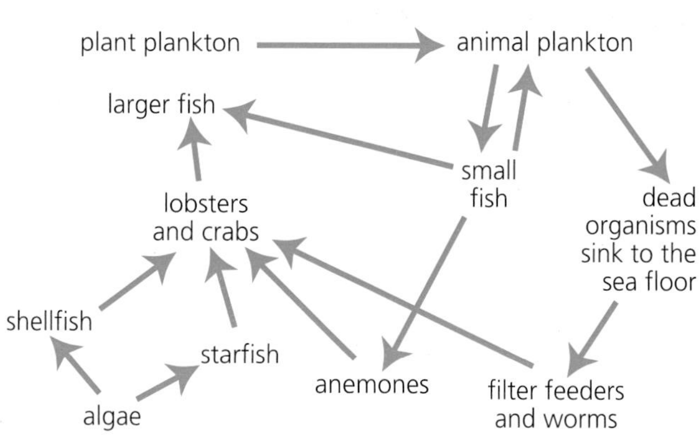

Imagine that the plant or animal named on the card has been completely removed from the food chain. Using the food web diagram identify three other plants or animals which could be affected by this. Try to explain what would happen to these organisms and why. Record two examples in the spaces below.

Name of organism removed from food chain ....

Effect on three other organisms

Organism	**Effect**
....	....
....	....
....	....

Name of organism removed from food chain ....

Effect on three other organisms

Organism	**Effect**
....	....
....	....
....	....

Populations can grow and grow ... 10

Do you ever do the weeding in a garden?

If you do, you will know how quickly weeds can appear again after you have done the weeding! Weed populations can increase quickly.

Something to do

1 Use your Classbook and list the things which can affect the size of a population.

- ....
- ....
- ....
- ....

2 What would happen if more animals in a population were born than died?

....

What would happen if more animals in a population died than were born?

....

3 Look at figure 3 on page 77 of your Classbook and fill in the table on the right.

	Numbers of hares	Numbers of lynx
1875		
1885		
1895		
1905		
1915		
1925		
1935		

4 Why do you think the numbers of hares and lynx go up and down in waves?

....

....

....

National Curriculum links

- Life processes and living things
- Living things in their environment

If you can explain the distribution and abundance of organisms in habitats, you are working at level 6.

Links with the Classbook

Unit 37
pages 76–77

11 Population investigation

Jennifer and Siobhan started a population of duckweed with five fronds (leaves).

They counted the number of fronds every three days. Their results are shown in the table.

Days from start of experiment	Number of fronds
0	5
3	7
6	9
9	12
12	16
15	21
18	28
21	37

Days from start of experiment	Number of fronds
24	49
27	65
30	85
33	100
36	120
39	125
42	121

1 Plot their results on a graph, putting time along the horizontal axis and number of fronds on the vertical axis. Draw a smooth curve as close to the points as you can.

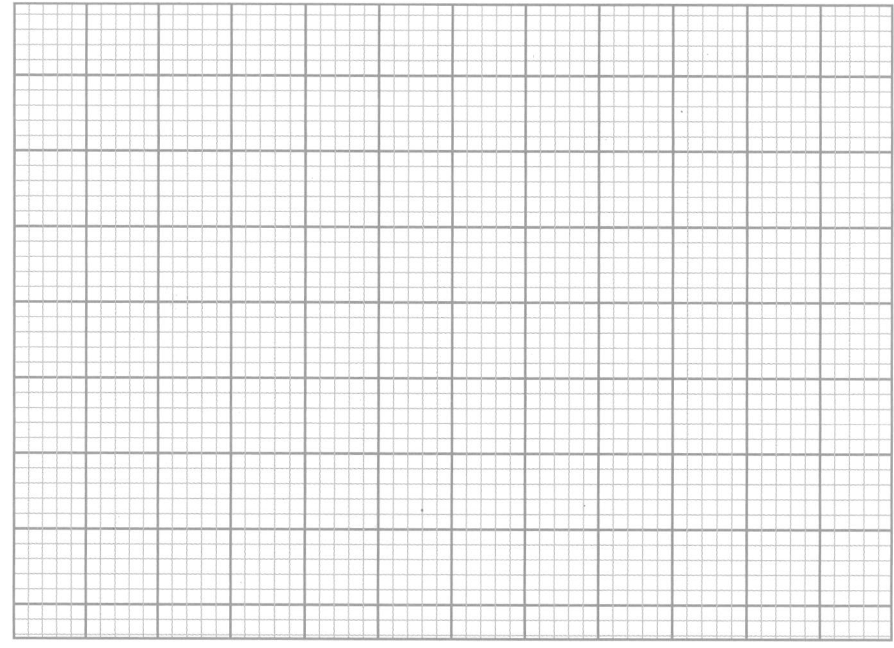

National Curriculum links

- Life processes and living things
- Living things in their environment
- Competition

If you can explain the distribution and abundance of organisms in habitats, you are working at level 6.

Links with the Classbook

Unit 37
pages 76–77

2 After the first 15 days Jennifer and Siobhan expected the final number of fronds to be more than 25.

Why do you think they expected this?

3 Suggest two reasons why the number of fronds decreased between 39 and 42 days

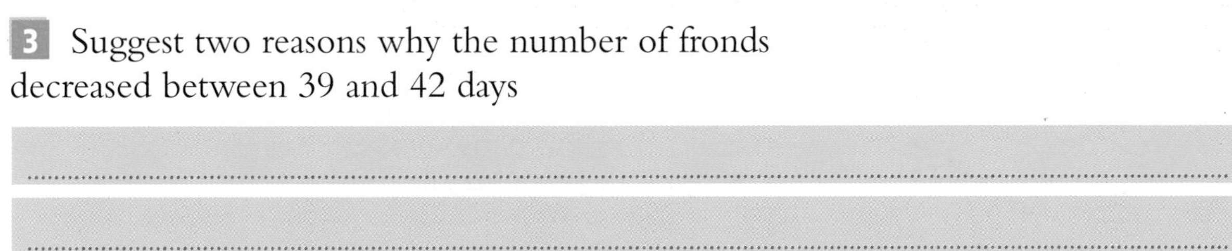

4 Choose one of the reasons you have suggested and say how you could carry out an investigation to test it.

The instructions below show how to use your calculator to model the growth of a population of rabbits.

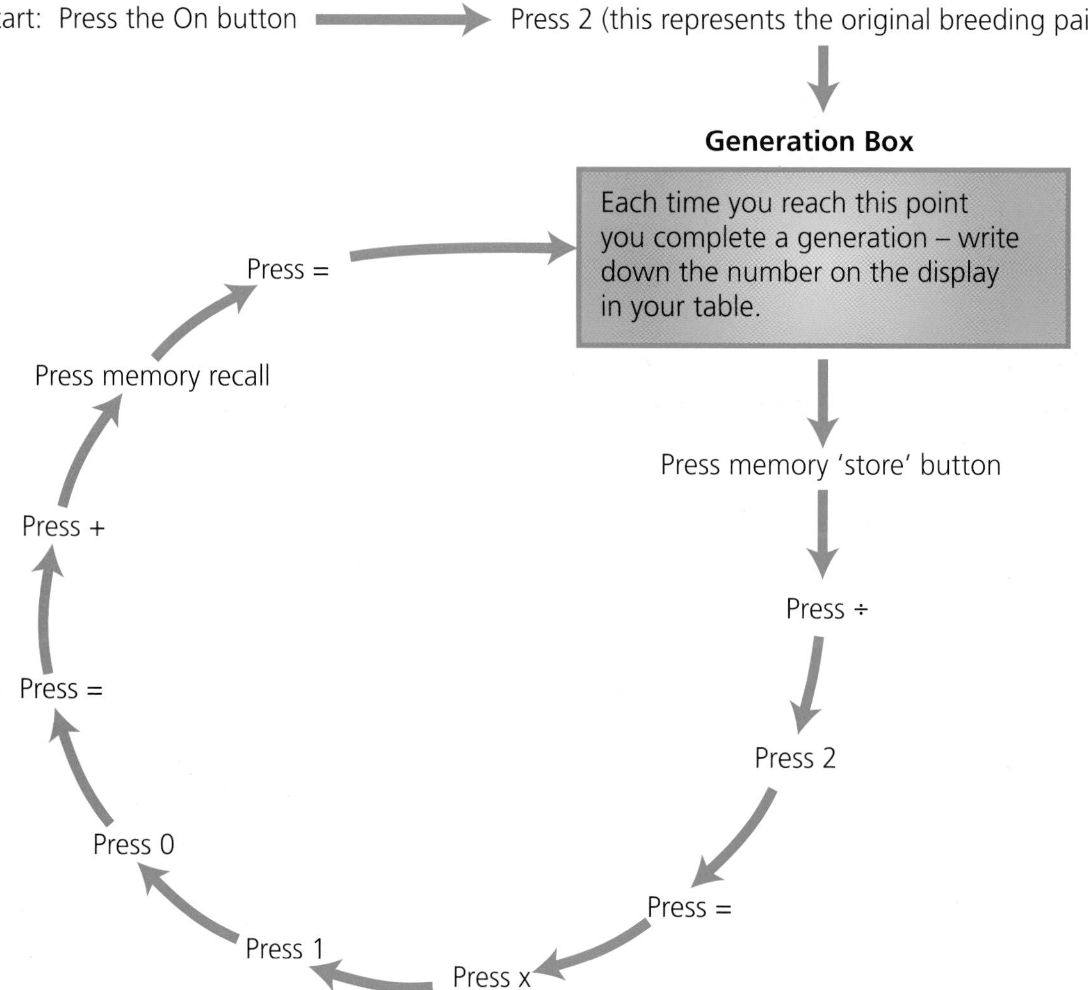
Start: Press the On button
Press 2 (this represents the original breeding pair)
Generation Box
Each time you reach this point you complete a generation – write down the number on the display in your table.
Press memory 'store' button
Press ÷
Press 2
Press =
Press x
Press 1
Press 0
Press =
Press +
Press memory recall
Press =

1 Begin with a pair of rabbits which produces a litter of 10 babies each time they breed (that is in each generation) so the first generation will be the original pair plus their 10 babies, i.e. 12, which is written in the table opposite for you.

Press the buttons on your calculator in the order shown. Put this number in the 'population increase' column of the table. Add the preceding generation to give the total population. Write down the number on your calculator each time you reach the 'generation' box.

The rabbits breed every 3 months so 8 times around the instructions will give you the population after 2 years.

Complete the table:

Generation	Time of year	Population increase	Total population
1	January	10	12
2	April		
3	July		
4	October		
5	January		
6	April		
7	July		
8	October		

2 The population after 2 years is unlikely to reach the number you calculated even if the rabbits did breed every 3 months and produced 10 babies each time.

Can you suggest some reasons for this?

(*Hint* – pages 76 and 77 of your Classbook will be helpful.)

....

....

....

....

....

....

....

....

12 Solid, liquid or gas?

The materials around us are found as **solids, liquids** or **gases**. These are called the **three states of matter**. To decide whether a particular material is solid, liquid or gas we need to think about its properties.

What to do

1 Working by yourself, think of three examples of solids. Then decide on three properties that help you to identify them as solids.

Share your ideas in a pair or group and record them in the table below.

Name of solid	Properties which show it is a solid

2 Repeat these steps to complete the tables below for liquids and gases. Remember to think of three examples on your own first.

Name of liquid	Properties which show it is a liquid

Name of gas	Properties which show it is a gas

3 In each table underline the properties which you all agree are typical of solids, liquids and gases.

Compare your tables with the information about properties of solids, liquids and gases given on pages 84 and 85 of your Classbook.

National Curriculum links

- Materials and their properties
- Classifying materials

If you can describe how particles are arranged in solids, liquids and gases you are working at level 6.

Links with the Classbook

Units 39 and 40
pages 84–87

The table below links a property of a solid, liquid or gas to the arrangement of particles.

4 Use these diagrams and the information on page 86 of your Classbook to complete the table below.

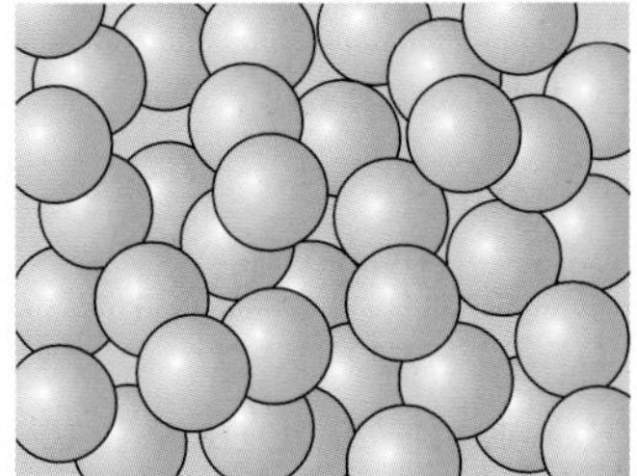

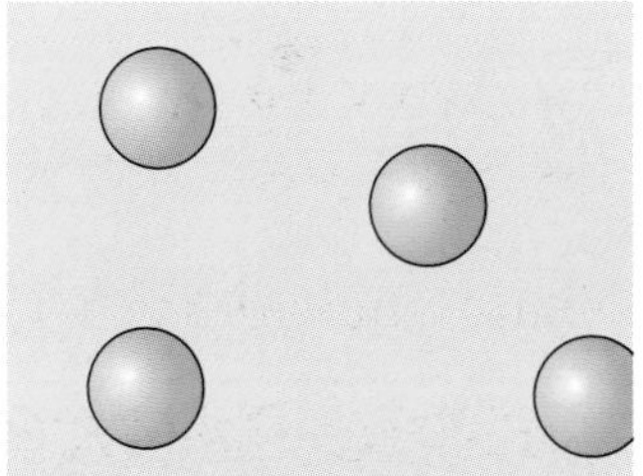

Arrangement of Particles	Property
in solids, the particles are packed close together and are arranged regularly	solids cannot be compressed
	liquids take on the shape of the container they are in
the particles in gases are widely spaced and move at great speeds	

5 Explain what the following terms mean:

a Particle theory ....

....

....

b Random motion ....

....

....

13 Explaining changes of state

A younger person asks you why water turns into ice when it has been in the freezer for a while. You explain to him that the water is made up of very small particles, and that the particles are arranged differently in solids and liquids. You decide that a diagram may help him to understand this idea.

What to do

1 Draw diagrams to show the arrangement of particles in ice and water. Write some brief notes in the boxes provided to explain how the particles would be arranged. Also write about what happens to the particles as they change from water to ice.

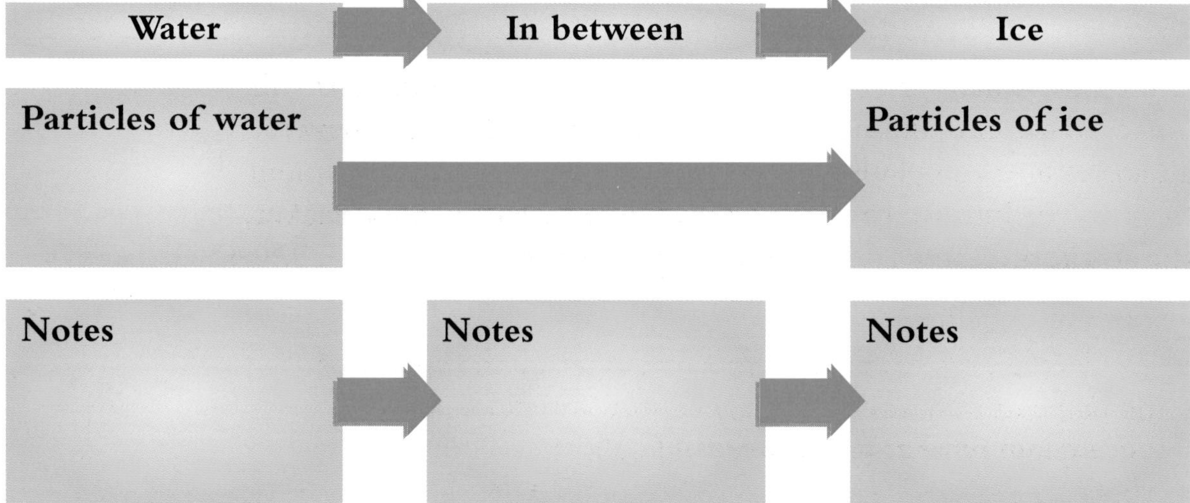

Later the same day, the person says he cannot play football outside because of the puddles on the yard. He says he will have to wait until the water has soaked into the ground. You explain to him that some of the water will evaporate, but this is a new idea to him.

2 Draw a diagram in the space on the next page to explain what happens to the particles in water during evaporation.

National Curriculum links

- Materials and their properties
- Classifying materials

To be working at level 7 you should be able to explain changes of state by describing the arrangement and behaviour of particles.

Links with the Classbook

Unit 40
pages 86–87

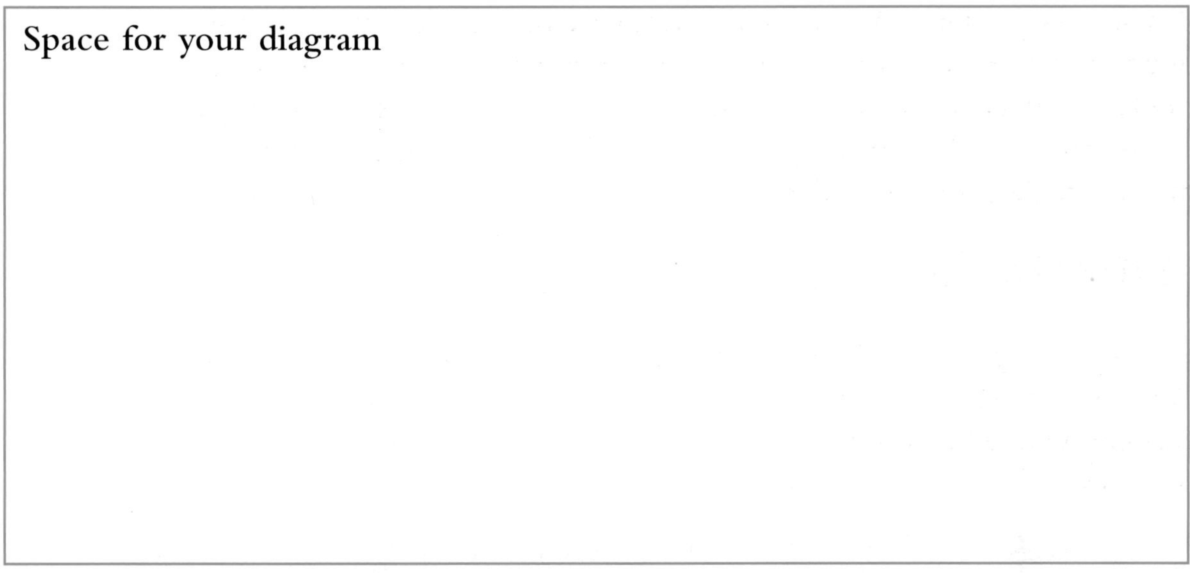

Even after studying your excellent diagrams the person is still not convinced that water can go into the air. He still thinks it all soaks into the ground. You decide to design an experiment to prove to him that water evaporates. You will need a beaker, water, thermometer and measuring cylinder.

3 In the space below:

a draw a diagram of how you would set up the apparatus

b explain how you would make sure you did a fair test

c explain what results you would collect.

Space for your diagram

14 Atomic clues

Mark Clueless, the well-known science crossword writer, has gone on holiday leaving his latest work unfinished. He has constructed the grid below showing the answers but has not made up the clues.

[1]P			[2]C	O	[3]M	P	O	U	N	D	S
R					O						
O				[4]E	L	E	C	T	R	O	N
T					E						
O					C			[5]A			
[6]N	U	[7]C	L	E	U	S		T			
		H			L			O			
		A			[8]E	L	E	M	E	N	T
		R			S						
		G									
		E									

What to do

1 In the spaces below write clues to complete the crossword. Use information from pages 90 to 93 of your Classbook to help you. Try to use a range of types of clue such as anagrams or picture clues.

Clues Down

1 ....

3 ....

5 ....

7 ....

Clues Across

2 ....

4 ....

6 ....

8 ....

2 The space below can be used to add extra clues if you want to extend the grid.

....

National Curriculum links

- Materials and their properties
- Classifying materials

To be working at level 7 you should be able to explain the difference between elements, mixtures and compounds.

Links with the Classbook

Units 42–43
pages 90–93

Symbols and formulae 15

Atoms and molecules can be represented by **symbols** and **formulae**. An individual element is shown by using its symbol. When elements join together to form compounds, the new molecules formed are shown by using a set of symbols called a formula.

What to do

1 In the table below join the correct symbol or formula on the left to the name or description on the right. An example is done for you.

Fe	The symbol for aluminium
CuO	The formula for ammonia
Al	The symbol for a metal which rusts
H_2O	The symbol for lead
NH_3	A very reactive metal
Pb	A non-metallic element, used to make chips
Si	The formula for a compound usually called salt
Cl	This compound is not usually called hydrogen oxide
Na	The symbol for chlorine
NaCl	The formula for a metal oxide

National Curriculum links

- Materials and their properties
- Classifying materials

To be working at level 7 you should be able to explain the difference between elements, mixtures and compounds and be able to use symbols and formulae to represent them.

If you can show that you understand that compounds have a definite composition, and can use formulae correctly, you would be working at level 7 to 8.

Links with the Classbook

Units 44, 45 and 46
pages 94–99

Writing formulae

There are some simple rules that you need to know when writing the shorthand for chemicals.

1 Write down the name of the compound. Be careful, some names are very similar.

2 Look up the symbols for the chemicals. Use a table of ions like the one below. Try to remember the most common ones.

3 Count the number of positive charges and the number of negative charges on the ions. Compounds do not have an electrical charge so these must eventually balance.

4 If you have too many positive charges, you must add more of the negative ions. If you have too many negative ions you must add more of the positive ions.

5 Once the charges are balanced you can write down the formula.

Example

Name	Copper	chloride
Symbols	Cu^{2+}	Cl^-

There are more positive charges than negative so we add extra chloride ions until the charges are balanced.

	Cu^{2+}	Cl^-
		Cl^-
Formula	$CuCl_2$	

The small 2 in $CuCl_2$ means that there are two chloride ions and one copper ion in copper chloride.

Table of ions

Positive ions		Negative ions	
Name	**Symbol and charge**	**Name**	**Symbol and charge**
ammonium	NH_4^+	chloride	Cl^-
sodium	Na^+	hydroxide	OH^-
copper	Cu^{2+}	nitrate	NO_3^-
magnesium	Mg^{2+}	carbonate	CO_3^{2-}
zinc	Zn^{2+}	oxide	O^{2-}
aluminium	Al^{3+}	sulphate	SO_4^{2-}

Examples for you to try

1 **a** copper oxide

b sodium chloride

c sodium sulphate

d magnesium chloride

e aluminium oxide

f ammonium nitrate

2 The formula for aluminium sulphate is $Al_2(SO_4)_3$

Explain what each of the numbers means.

....

....

....

3 Why does this formula need to contain brackets?

....

16 Predicting reactions

Many compounds are formed when a metal and non-metal element react together. Some pairs of metals and non-metals react quickly and violently but other pairs will not react at all. Below is a list of metal and non-metal elements shown by their symbols.

Na	Br	Mg	Ag	Ne
F	Si	S	Cu	Cr

What to do

1 On the list, circle the elements which are metals.

2 Using the information on pages 96 and 97 of your Classbook and the Periodic Table shown on page 243, write down the **names** of one pair of elements which you think:

a would react violently together

b would not react at all

c would probably react fairly easily but safely

d would probably only react together if they were heated to speed up the process.

3 In the space below, write down the names of three examples of compounds formed.

National Curriculum links

- Materials and their properties
- Changing materials

To be working at level 7 you should be able to use patterns of reactivity to make predictions about particular chemical reactions.

Links with the Classbook

Unit 45
pages 96–97

Volcanoes and crystals 17

Molten rock, or **magma**, from deep inside the Earth can reach the surface. When this happens the magma cools and becomes solid rock. Rocks formed in this way are called **igneous rocks**.

1 Read the information below.

Magma that reaches the surface cools very quickly. This rapid cooling does not give much time for crystals to grow. This means that igneous rocks that have cooled quickly contain very small crystals. Many can only be seen with a microscope.

Magma that cools deep underground turns into a solid very slowly. This gives the crystals a long time to grow. This means that igneous rocks that have cooled very slowly contain very large crystals. Some are more than 3 cm long.

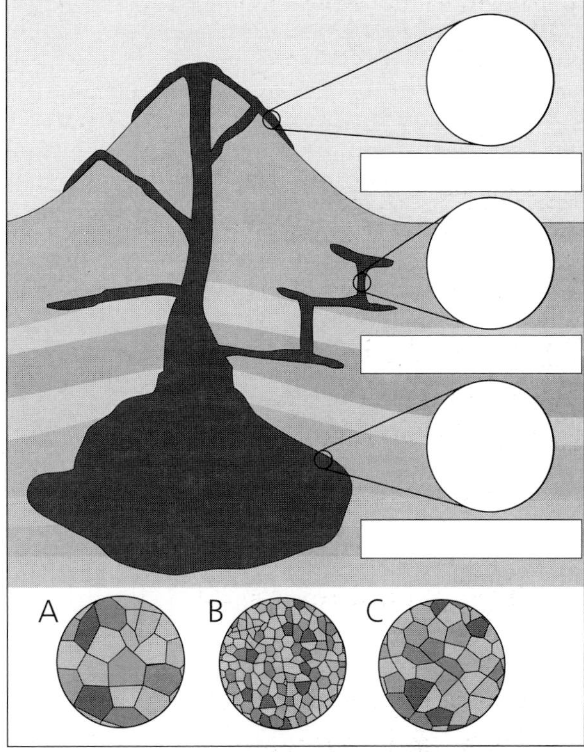

2 Label the diagram on the right.

a Select the correct crystal size from three choices.

b Try to find examples of each type of rock and write them in the boxes.

3 Explain what happens to magma as it cools deep underground. Include the following words in your description.

energy crystals cooling transfer igneous solid state

....

....

....

National Curriculum links

- Materials and their properties
- Changing materials

If you can use the formation of igneous rocks as an example of what happens to energy as materials change state you would be working at level 6.

Links with the Classbook

Unit 57
pages 120–121

18 Word equations

The names of compounds can be written down in a shorthand way as chemical formulae. This is also true of chemical reactions. The shorthand way of writing down a chemical reaction is called an **equation**.

What to do

1 Read the following descriptions and then write them down as word equations.

a Some small pieces of calcium carbonate were added to hydrochloric acid. The reaction gave off carbon dioxide gas. A salt called calcium chloride was made and another product was water.

b When zinc was added to copper sulphate solution, a salt called zinc sulphate was made. The copper was found as a metal in the mixture.

c If calcium carbonate is heated very strongly, it breaks down to give calcium oxide and carbon dioxide gas.

2 Look at the word equations below. For each one write a short description of what is happening during the chemical reaction.

a lead oxide + magnesium $\rightarrow$ lead + magnesium oxide

....

....

b zinc + sulphuric acid $\rightarrow$ zinc sulphate + hydrogen

....

....

National Curriculum links

- Materials and their properties
- Changing materials

If you can use word equations to describe chemical reactions you are working at level 6.

Links with the Classbook

Unit 62
pages 130–131

When a chemical reaction takes place, all the chemicals involved can be written down in a word equation. The chemical or chemicals which react are called the **reactants**. The chemical or chemicals that are produced are called the **products**. An arrow (→) usually separates the reactants and products.

1 Look at the eight reactions below. In each case, work out the name of the missing chemical and write it into the word equation.

a magnesium + ... → magnesium sulphate + copper

b .... + hydrochloric acid → copper chloride + water + carbon dioxide

c calcium + ... → calcium oxide + hydrogen

d .... → calcium oxide + carbon dioxide

e magnesium + ... → magnesium nitrate + hydrogen

f carbon + ... → carbon dioxide + iron

g zinc + oxygen → zinc ....

h nitric acid + sodium hydroxide → .... + water

2 Write out your answers into the grid below. If you have worked out the names of the chemicals correctly, a word will be made in the spine of the grid.

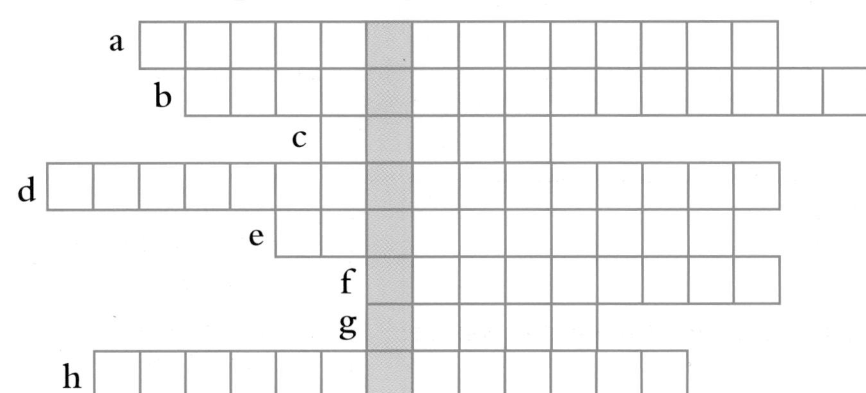

19 Oxidation and reduction

When any chemical joins with oxygen during a chemical reaction we say that it has been **oxidised.** If a chemical loses oxygen during a chemical reaction we say it has been **reduced.**

The diagram on the right shows copper oxide being heated in a stream of hydrogen gas.

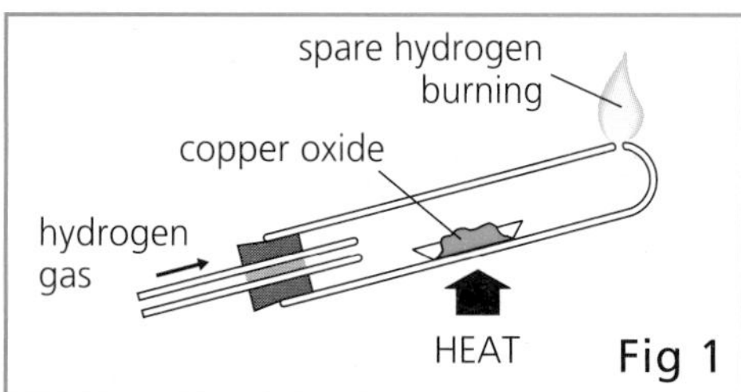

Fig 1

1 Write down an important safety rule that a person heating chemicals must follow.

....

2 The copper oxide is changed into copper metal. Is the copper oxidised or reduced?

....

3 The hydrogen is changed to hydrogen oxide (water). Is the hydrogen oxidised or reduced?

....

Many metals gradually react with oxygen in the air to form oxides. This is called **corrosion.** The diagram on the right is taken from your Classbook, page 136. Read pages 136–137 of your Classbook and answer the following questions.

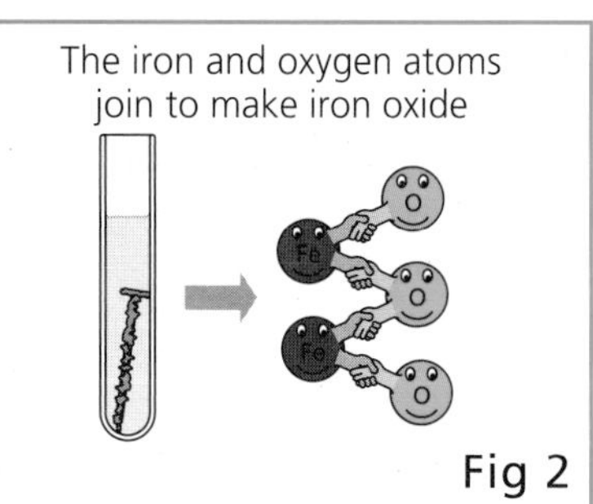

The iron and oxygen atoms join to make iron oxide
Fe
O

Fig 2

4 List two things that speed up corrosion.

a .... **b** ....

5 Rust is mainly iron oxide. Is iron oxidised or reduced when it rusts?

....

6 Show figure 2 as a word equation. Use the space below.

....

National Curriculum links

- Materials and their properties
- Changing materials

If you can use word equations to describe how oxygen reacts with some chemicals you are working at level 6.

Links with the Classbook

Units 63 and 65
pages 132–133 and 136–137

As a metal is oxidised it becomes less strong. This is because oxides are more powdery than the original metal. You may have seen this with some iron and steel objects at home. We call this type of corrosion **rusting**.

The process

1 Change the paragraph opposite into a flow diagram. Use the boxes provided below.

> The surface of a metal will react with oxygen to form an oxide. The first visible sign of corrosion is when an object loses its shine. A layer of oxide dulls the surface. Cracks and holes in the surface get bigger. This speeds up rusting even more. Corrosion will spread. The metal becomes thinner and the cracks widen. Eventually the metal may become so weak it breaks.

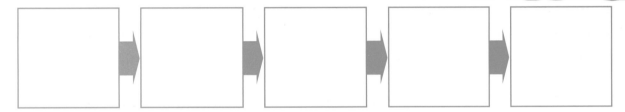

A space mystery

Objects have been left on the Moon since the 1960's. However, none of them have corroded.

2 Write down one possible reason for this.

....

We are not so lucky on Earth. Metal objects quickly corrode. However, we can try to prevent this from happening.

3 Select a steel object from your house or garden. In the space below make a list of the possible ways it could be prevented from rusting.

....

....

4 Finally, on a separate piece of paper, design a small instruction sheet that tells people how to look after the steel object so that it will remain in good condition for as long as possible.

20 Acids and alkalis

1 Each of the substances shown opposite has a certain pH value. Draw a line from the dot by the substance to the dot by the correct pH value. If you have done this correctly, each line will pass through a letter. When you have finished, the letters with lines through will make a word.

Substance	Letters					pH
lemon juice ●			D			● 1
		N				● 2
					O	● 3
oven cleaner ●		S	E			● 4
	U					
soap ●				W		● 5
						● 6
car battery ● acid		M	T			● 7
						● 8
	R	A		L		● 9
water ●			E			● 10
		A				● 11
soda water ●			L	U		● 12
						● 13
washing soda ●		P		N		● 14

Sprays and liquids are now available to soothe wasp and bee stings.

Before these medicines were available people used vinegar or baking powder. When a bee stings, a small amount of acid is injected into the skin. A wasp injects a small amount of alkali.

2 Would you use vinegar (an acid) or baking powder (an alkali) for:

a a bee sting?	acid vinegar	yes	no	alkali baking powder	yes	no
b a wasp sting?	acid vinegar	yes	no	alkali baking powder	yes	no

3 In the laboratory we can neutralise acids with alkalis. In the space below write a word equation for hydrochloric acid being neutralised by adding sodium hydroxide.

....

4 What is the pH of the solution when it is neutralised?

....

5 What would happen to the pH of the mixture if you added too much alkali?

....

National Curriculum links

■ Materials and their properties ■ Patterns of behaviour

To be working at level 6 you should be able to describe some of the reactions of acids.

To be working at level 6 you should be able to describe how limestone reacts with rainwater.

Links with the Classbook

Units 73, 74, 75 and 76
pages 152–159

Gerry and Ahmed are walking past some statues and gravestones. Most of them are made of limestone or marble. 'Lots of these look like they are wearing away' says Gerry. 'Yes,' answers Ahmed 'but some seem to be lasting longer than others.'
Ahmed is pointing at two nearby limestone gravestones. One is so damaged that it is difficult to read the writing on it. The other is in very good condition.

6 Explain why one gravestone is more worn away than the other.

....

Erosion of gravestones and statues has become worse in recent years. This is because of acid rain.

7 What is acid rain?

....

....

8 Explain how acid rain causes damage to objects made from limestone and marble. Remember that these rocks are made up of calcium carbonate.

....

....

Ahmed remembers that one of the old gravestones near the church was in good condition. His science teacher explains that it was possibly made out of granite.

9 Write a brief paragraph describing how you could compare the reactions of granite and limestone with a laboratory acid such as hydrochloric acid.

....

....

....

....

21 Calculating speed

Seven pupils ran as fast as they could for a certain distance. The time taken to run each distance was measured with a stopwatch. The group then calculated the average speed for each person. Anita quickly copied the results into her book but missed out some figures.

This is their results table:

Name	Distance travelled (m)	Time taken (s)	Average speed (m/s)
Anita	25	5	5
Brendan	24	4	
Colin	20		4
Diana		8	3
Vikram	30		10
Fiona	24	6	
Guy		7	4

1 Work out the figures that Anita missed out and add them to the table.

2 A man cycles 10 km in 30 minutes. He then rests for 60 minutes. He cycles a further 10 km during the next 30 minutes.

a On the graph add lines which show the distance travelled by the cyclist.

b What is the average speed of the cyclist during:

- the first 30 minutes ....
- the time he was resting ....
- the last 30 minutes ....
- the whole journey. ....

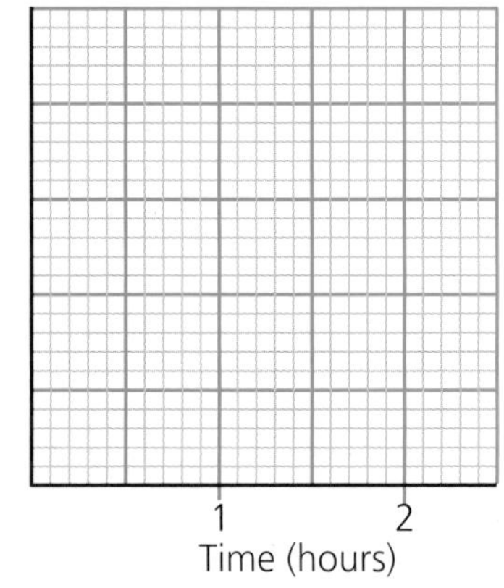

National Curriculum links

- Physical processes
- Forces and motion

To be working at level 7 you need to know how to use the formula v=d/t.

Links with the Classbook

Unit 77 and 78
pages 164–167

When you travel home from school, you cover the distance in a certain time. For example, Myra lives 2 km from school and it takes her 20 minutes to walk home.

1 What is Myra's average speed for her journey home? ....

When you travel home, you are unlikely to travel at exactly the same speed all of the way. You may stop to talk. You may be slower up hills than down. You may even catch a bus some of the way! How can you show this more realistic version of a journey?

On pages 166 and 167 of your Classbook **distance-time graphs** are shown. These graphs are a useful way of showing a journey. The graph is made by plotting how much distance is covered during each stage or leg of a jouney.

Your distance-time graph

2 Work out a distance-time graph for your journey to or from school. Draw the graph on the paper provided.

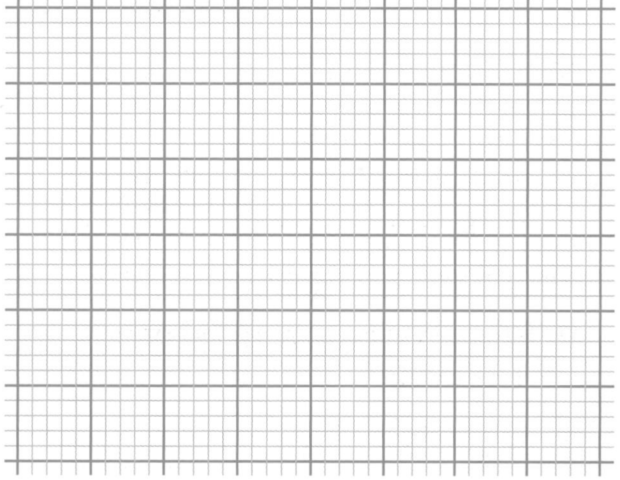

3 What is your average speed for the total journey? ....

4 Label the fastest part of your journey by placing an A on your graph.

What is your average speed for this part of the journey? ....

5 Label the slowest part of your journey by placing a B on your graph.

What is your average speed for this part of the journey? ....

6 If you wish, you could use the graph paper to add a distance-time graph for another member of your family.

22 The law of moments

The force around a **pivot** is called the **moment.**

1 In the space below state the **law of moments**.

....

2 Which of the following will have the largest moment of force?

a A large person sitting close to the pivot.
b A small person sitting away from the pivot.
c A large person sitting away from the pivot.

Explain your answer

....

....

The table below shows the results of an experiment with a seesaw. David and Shanaz are balancing a seesaw by adding masses to one side or the other. They also look at how far from the pivot the masses were placed. They have changed mass to force in their results table as they know that every 10g they add is equal to one extra Newton. Some results are missing.

3 Complete their table by working out the missing values.
The equation on page 172 of your Classbook could be useful!

	Side 1			Side 2		
	Distance from pivot (m)	Force (N)	Moment (Nm)	Distance from pivot (m)	Force (N)	Moment (Nm)
A	1	200	200	1	200	200
B	1.5	300		1.5		600
C	2		400	2	100	
D	2.5	200		2.5		500
E	3		900	3	250	

4 In which experiments is the seesaw balanced? ....

National Curriculum links
■ Physical processes ■ Forces and motion
If you can calculate and explain moments you are working at level 7.

Links with the Classbook
Unit 81
pages 172–173

Many sports use turning forces.

1 Describe how the pole vaulter is using turning forces to clear the bar.

....

....

....

....

....

....

....

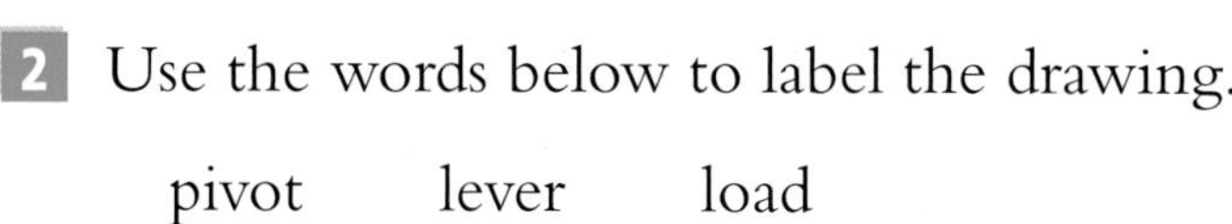

2 Use the words below to label the drawing.

pivot lever load

3 Make a list of two other examples of turning forces in sports.

a ....

b ....

4 Draw one of these examples and label the pivot.

Space for your diagram

5 Why do weightlifters try to raise the weights above their heads as quickly as possible?

Hint – think about levers, moments and try holding a weight at arm's length in front of you!

....

23 The planets

Data relating to the planets is readily available from a variety of sources including textbooks and CD-ROMs. You can find out information about mass, diameter, gravity and distance from the Sun, for example.

Graphs can be plotted to test different hypotheses.

- Do planets with greater masses have more gravity?
- Do planets further away from the Sun have less gravity?
- As you move further away from the Sun does the surface temperature of a planet decrease?

1 Choose a hypothesis from the list or make up your own. Write it down here.

....

2 Write down what you predict you will find out.

....

....

3 Collect the appropriate data to plot a graph which includes each of the nine planets. Complete the table on the page opposite with your data.

4 Plot your graph on the graph paper provided.

5 Was your hypothesis correct?

....

....

6 Were there any exceptions? If there were, can you explain why the planet didn't follow the pattern of the others?

....

....

....

National Curriculum links

- Physical processes
- The Earth and beyond

To be working at level 8 you should be able to obtain data and use your knowledge to explain any patterns in the data.

Links with the Classbook

Units 84 and 85
pages 178–181

Planet	Mercury	Venus	Earth	Mars	Jupiter	Saturn	Uranus	Neptune	Pluto

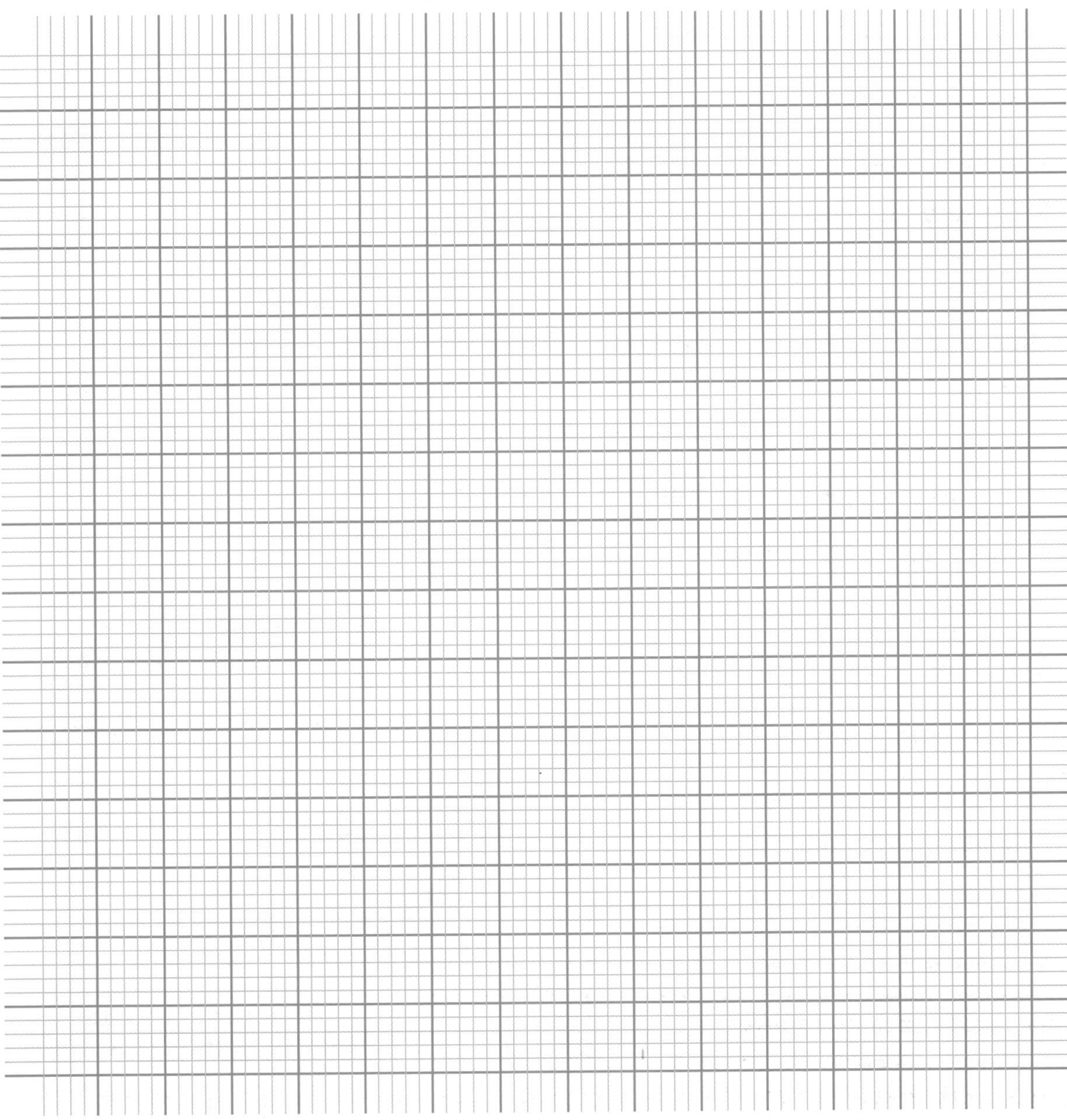

24 Light and colour

When light passes from a less dense medium to a more dense medium it is bent or **refracted.** The same happens when light passes from a more dense to a less dense medium. Light from the Sun is called **white light.**

1 Use the information on page 204 of your Classbook to label the diagrams below.

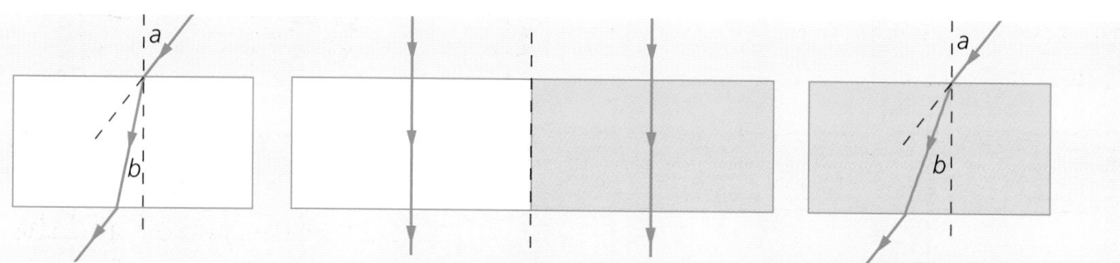

2 Is the angle of incidence a) or b) in each diagram? ....

3 Is the angle of refraction a) or b) in each diagram? ....

White light is a mixture of **seven** different colours. Each of these seven colours can be bent or refracted, but they are bent by different amounts. As a result a prism can split white light to make a **spectrum.**

A good way to remember the sequence of the seven colours is by learning the phrase:

***R**ichard*	***O**f*	***Y**ork*	***G**ave*	***B**attle*	***I**n*	***V**ain*
Red	Orange	Yellow	Green	Blue	Indigo	Violet

A rainbow is caused by white light from the Sun being refracted by droplets of water in the air.

4 Complete the diagram to show how a rainbow is formed.

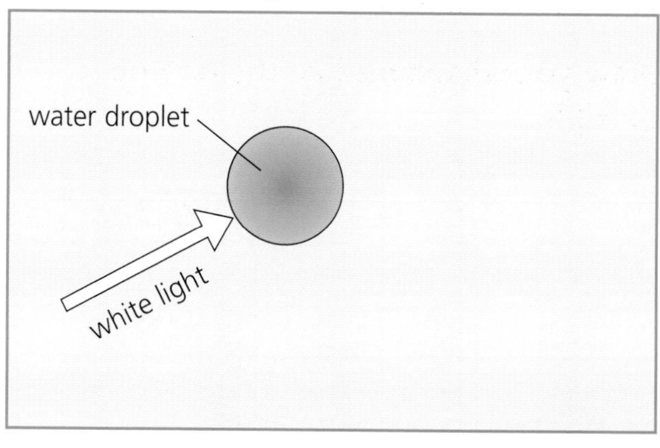

National Curriculum links

■ Physical processes ■ Sound and light

To be working at level 6 you should be able to recognise refraction and apply the principle to new contexts.

To be working at level 7 you need to explain the appearance of objects in different colours of light.

Links with the Classbook

Units 97, 98 and 99
pages 204–209

Jack is watching a singer performing on stage.

The lighting technicians shine lights onto the stage. They can shine three different colours. These colours are red, green and blue.

Part of scene	Red light	Green light	Blue light
T-shirt			
trousers			
background			
curtains			
floor			

5 Complete the table by adding the colour of each part of the person and the stage when each of the three coloured lights are used.

6 Choose one part of the scene, for example the T-shirt, and draw three diagrams to explain the answers that you have put in the table.

Draw your diagrams like the one on the right.

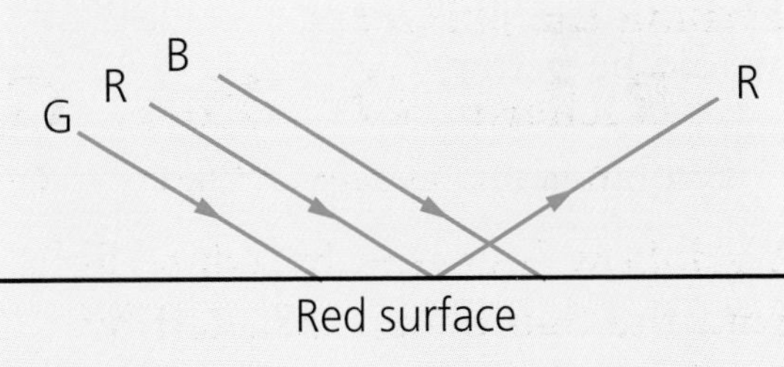

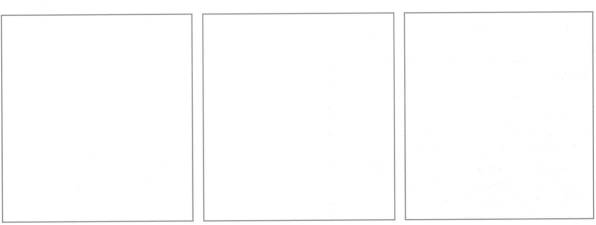

We live in a world of colour. All around us colour is used to warn us, attract us, excite us, calm us and entertain us.

1 List two examples of colours being used in the following situations:

a as a warning of danger

....

....

b to create mood or atmosphere

....

....

c to help in selling products.

....

....

2 A new tinned food has been produced. The makers have put a bright red label on the can to attract customers. A supermarket manager is using blue and green lights to highlight the product. Explain why white light would be better.

Explanation
Diagram

1 Use the words in the list below to complete the following paragraph.

All substances are made of .... These contain positively charged .... and negatively charged .... Most atoms contain the same .... of .... and .... The substance is electrically .... because the electrical charges are ....

protons electrons balanced atoms neutral number

Static Charge

Friction can remove electrons from one surface to another. This makes a static charge.

2 What type of charge is created when electrons are gained by a substance?

....

3 What type of charge is created when electrons are lost from a substance?

....

4 Complete the diagrams below by drawing what you think will happen in each case.

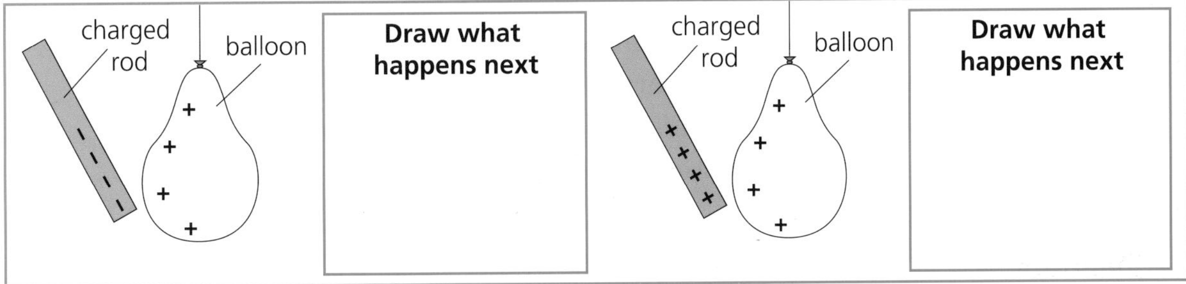

National Curriculum links

■ Physical processes ■ Electricity and magnetism

To be working at level 6 you should be able to explain that static electricity is caused by the gain or loss of electrons.

If you can use the idea of moving electrons to explain how a component works you are working at level 6.

Links with the Classbook

Unit 100 to 104
pages 210–219

What to do

1 Use your knowledge of electricity to complete the crossword puzzle.

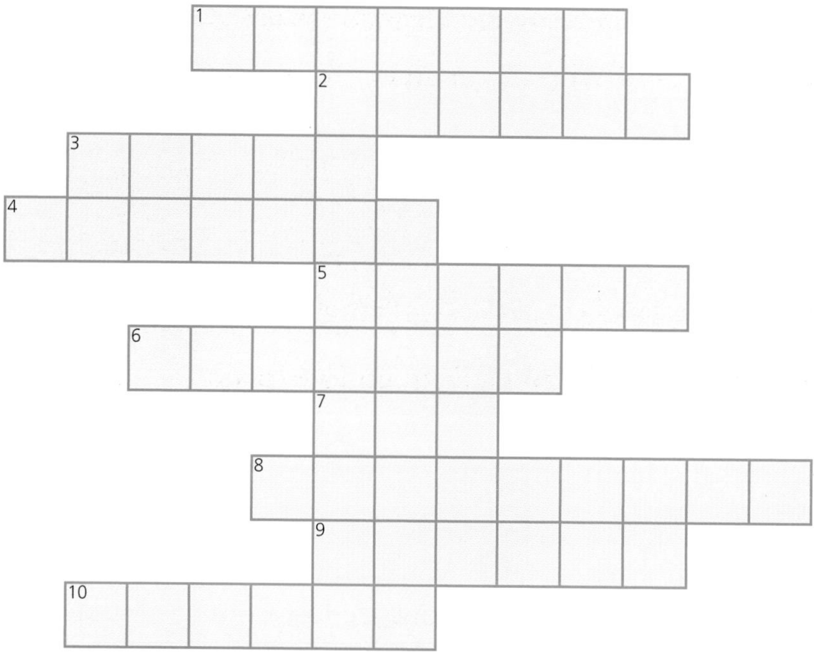

Clues

Across

1 The flow of charge.
2 A battery changes the chemical form of this to the electrical form.
3 These have a filament that glows brightly when it heats up.
4 This must be complete before electricity will flow.
5 These can be used to make or break a circuit.
6 A cell.
7 The unit of current.
8 This will not let electricity flow along it.
9 This can be positive or negative.
10 This type of circuit has bulbs in a row.

2 What is the mystery word hidden in the puzzle?

The word is:

3 Write a clue for the mystery word so that it can be added to the crossword as 1 down. Try your clue on other people in your group to see if it makes sense.

....

4 Make a list of **three** examples of why the mystery word is so important to us.

- ....
- ....
- ....

5 Choose one of your examples and draw a diagram to explain how it works.

Space for your diagram

6 Try to imagine a world where the mystery word does not exist. In the space below list some of the problems that would be caused and some of the inventions we would have to live without.

....

....

....

....

26 Magnetism

Becoming an expert

Imagine you are part of a public relations company. Your small team has been sent this letter.

Your group is determined to take on this interesting task. You will need to know a great deal about magnets and especially electromagnets. Together you will share the work, so that you each go away and research one part of the topic. Use the meeting agenda below to organise your group and to carry out the tasks.

Electro Company

Dear Colleagues,

Electro Company is one of the largest producers of magnets and electromagnets in the world. Our magnets have many uses and we have built up a good reputation for reliability. We are hoping to expand our business into new markets. In order to do this we require a publicity brochure.

Your public relations company has an excellent reputation for producing high quality brochures and we would like you to design one for us. I have made a list of the major points we would wish the brochure to contain. Could I also remind you of the need for all the scientific information to be properly checked and accurate.

The brochure must explain:

- what magnets are and what we mean by magnetic materials
- how we measure the strength of magnets
- technical terms such as *field, poles, repel* and *attract*
- what electromagnets are
- how electromagnets can be made stronger
- what electromagnets can be used for.

I am looking forward to seeing the design for the brochure.

Yours sincerely,

J. Steel

- It will help if you elect a chairperson.
- Keep to the time limits.

Agenda

1 Make sure each team member has read the letter from Electro Company. 5 mins

2 There are four expert tasks on the following pages. Choose one person to carry out each task. 20 mins

3 Split up and work through the expert tasks. You may be asked to work with experts from other groups. 20 mins

4 Report back from your expert group. Share your expertise by helping your team to complete their blank expert sheets. 25 mins

5 When you have *all* completed *all* of the expert sheets, work together to draft a rough copy of a brochure for Electro Company. Remember to include all of their requirements.

Homework

Complete a final version of the publicity brochure.

Expert Group 1 Navigation and magnetic substances

Carry out these tasks and report back to your research team.

One of the oldest uses for magnetism is the compass needle. If you dangle a small magnetic bar on the end of a thread, it will turn until it lines up in a north-south direction.

1 What are the ends of a bar magnet called? ....

The compass needle points north-south because the Earth is also a giant magnet. The compass needle lines up with the Earth's magnetic field.

What to do

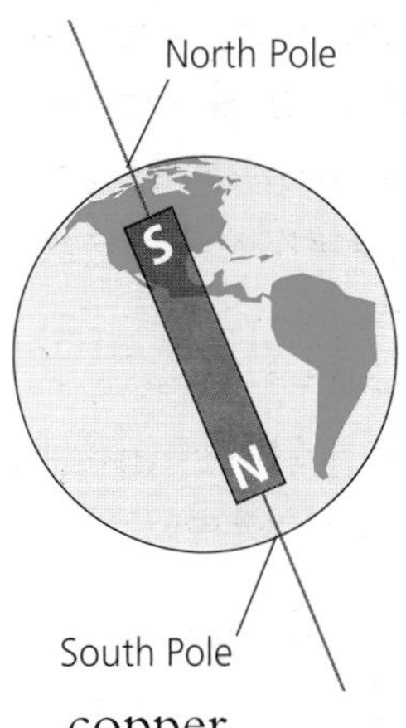

2 Complete the diagram opposite by drawing in the Earth's magnetic field.

Most substances are not magnetic. Non-metals are not magnetic. Iron and steel are the most important magnetic metals. Nickel and cobalt are also magnetic.

3 Circle the materials that could be made into magnets.

lead plastic iron paper wood nickel steel copper

As a group

4 Plan how you would develop a way to test quickly whether a metal bar is magnetic.

5 Discuss how you would make a reliable compass using a piece of card, string, sticky tape and a magnetic iron bar.

Links with the Classbook

Unit 105, 106 and 107
pages 220–225

National Curriculum links

- Physical Processes
- Electricity and magnetism

If you can explain about the shape and strength of a magnetic field you are working at level 6. If you can explain the strength of electromagnets you are working at level 7. If you can apply your ideas of electricty and magnetism to explain some uses of electromagnets you are working at level 5. If you can complete the graphs and explain the data you are working at level 6. If you can explain the link between electricity and magnetism you are working at level 7.

Expert Group 2 Magnetic fields

Carry out these tasks and report back to your research team.

When you slowly bring a metal object towards a magnet, you will notice the pull of the magnet before the object touches the magnet. Magnetism must be reaching out into the air around the magnet. We can use iron filings to make a pattern around a magnet.

1 Complete the diagram by drawing on the field patterns that would form.

Each filing behaves like a tiny compass needle. The lines show the magnetic field around the magnet. Tightly packed lines show where the field is strongest.

2 Label the strongest parts of the field on the diagram.

The north pole of one magnet will repel the north pole of another. The magnets will push apart. If the north pole of one magnet is pointed towards the south pole of another magnet they will be pulled together.

3 Tick the correct answer in each case.

a similar poles	attract		repel	
b opposite poles	attract		repel	

As a group

4 Plan how you would develop a way to show whether opposite poles of a magnet repel or attract.

5 Discuss how you would find out which of two bar magnets was the strongest. Would lines of force help?

Expert Group 3 Electricity and magnetism

Carry out these tasks and report back to your research team.

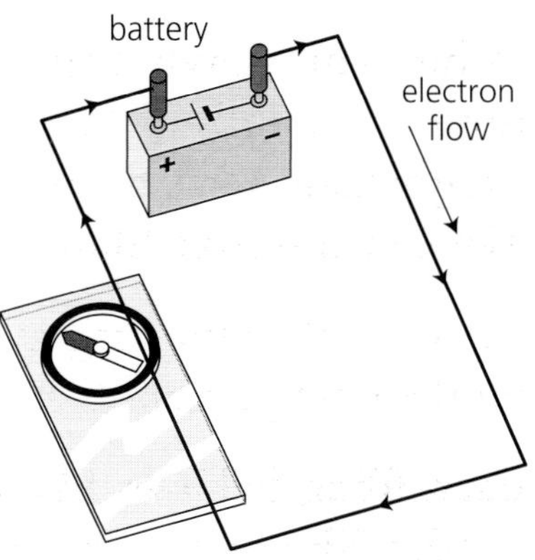

1 Study the diagram on the right. Show what happens to the compass needle when the battery is connected and the current flows down the wire.

2 On the diagram below, draw in the needles for the plotting compasses.

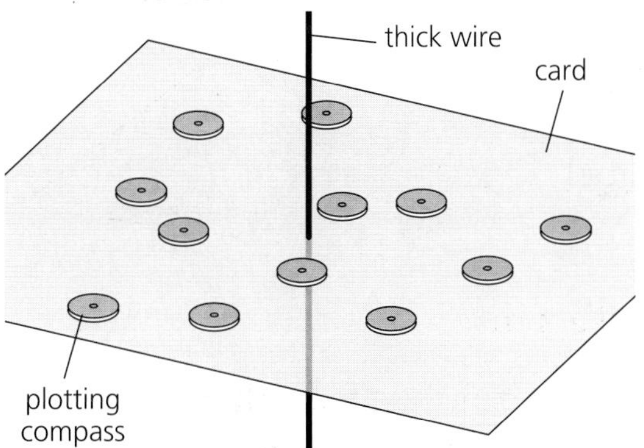

3 What do the compasses tell you about the magnetic field pattern around the wire? ....

In electromagnets the wire is coiled to make a stronger magnet. The more coils there are, the stronger the magnet will be. Another way to increase the strength of an electromagnet is to pass more current through the wire. It is also possible to coil the wire around a metal core to improve the strength of an electromagnet.

4 List three ways to make an electromagnet stronger.

....

....

....

As a group

5 Plan how you would develop a way to test whether increasing the number of coils will increase the strength of an electromagnet.

6 Discuss which variables you would keep the same in each case.

7 What measurements will you take?

Expert Group 4 Uses of electromagnets

Carry out these tasks and report back to your research team.

Electromagnets have many uses. One reason for this is that they can be made more powerful than ordinary magnets. They can also be switched on and off.

1 Why is it useful to be able to turn a magnet on and off?

....

Electric bells

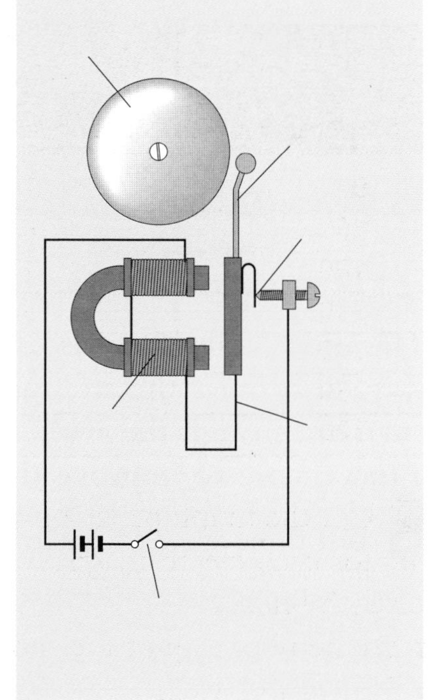

2 Read the information below and use it to label the diagram to the right.

An electric bell contains an electromagnet. The circuit is closed by pushing the bell push. When the current starts to flow it turns on the electromagnet. This immediately attracts a metal arm called an armature. The armature hits the gong. As the armature is pulled towards the gong the circuit is broken.

The electromagnet stops working and the armature springs away from the gong. This completes the circuit again and the whole process begins again. The gong can be struck many times in a few seconds.

3 Why would an electric bell not work with an ordinary magnet inside it instead of an electromagnet?

....

....

When a current flows through a wire, the wire has a magnetic field around it. The magnetic field around an ordinary wire is not very strong. We can make it stronger by coiling the wire, especially if we coil it around a metal core. The coil and the core together are called an **electromagnet**.

What to do

Look at the data in the table below. The figures show you how well different electromagnets can attract paper clips. In each case exactly the same current is used, but the electromagnets have different cores. The current is 4 amps.

	Strength of electromagnet (number of paper clips attracted)			
Number of coils	**Glass core**	**Air core**	**Steel core**	**Iron core**
0	0	0	0	0
50	0	0	2	4
100	2	2	4	7
150	3	3	6	10
200	4	4	8	14
250	4	5	11	16
300	6	7	13	20

1 Use the graph paper on page 58 to plot the data. You can plot the line for each electromagnet on the same graph. Use different colours for each line.

- Remember to plot the independent variable on the x axis.
- Remember to plot the dependent variable on the y axis.

2 Study the graph and explain what the data tells you about the different cores.

....

....

....

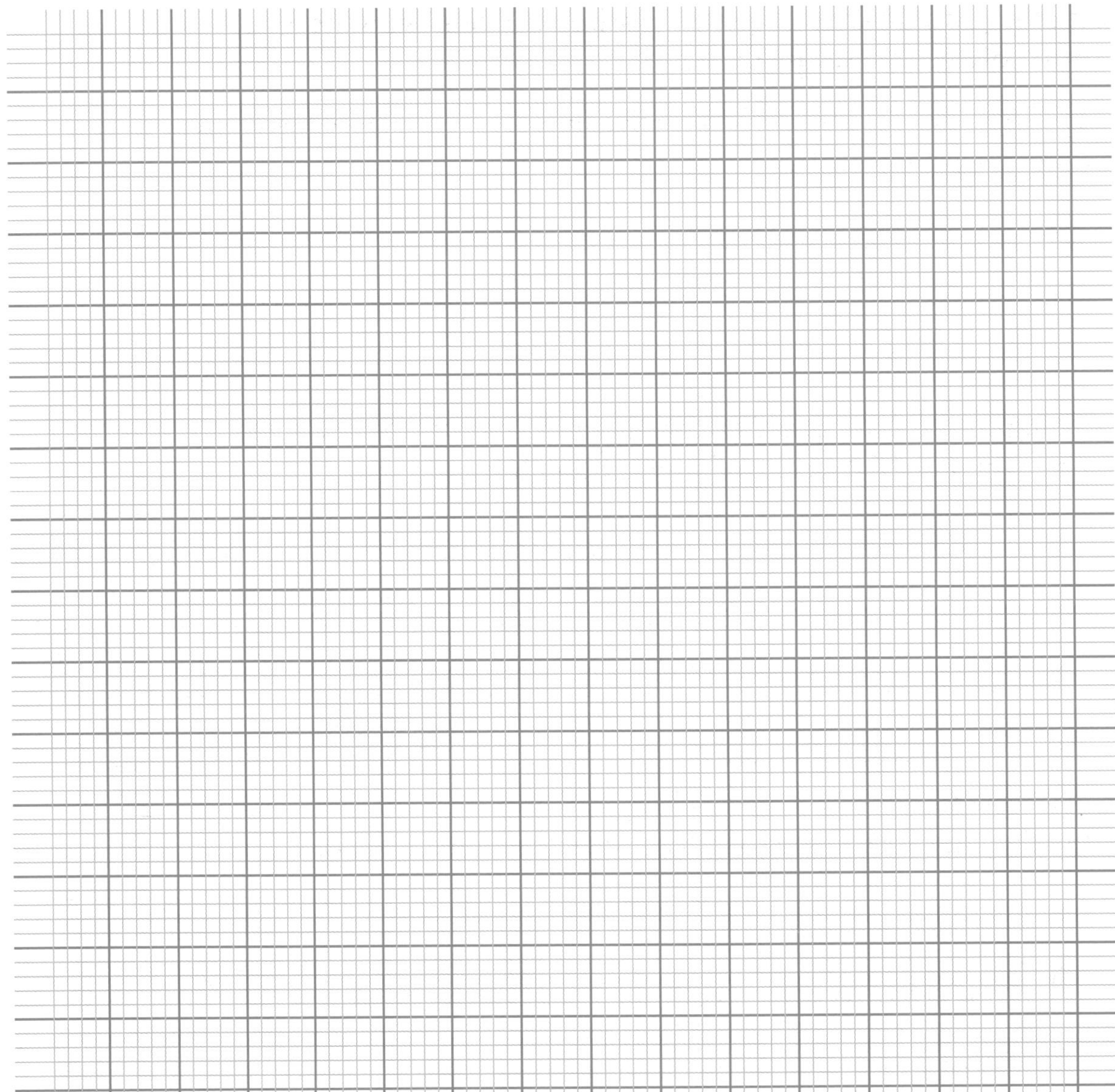

3 Use your knowledge of electromagnets to predict what the results would be for an iron core with 200 coils at 0, 1, 2, 4 and 8 amps.

Current (amps)	Number of paper clips attracted
0	
1	
2	
4	
8	

Alternative energy 27

Read pages 230–231 of your Classbook. Then, working in a group, discuss these questions.

1 There are a number of alternative energy sources now being used. Write down three of these.

a ....

b ....

c ....

2 Suggest how we could encourage the use of these alternative energy sources. Make a list of your group's four best ideas.

a ....

b ....

c ....

d ....

3 People seem to be slow to change away from using fossil fuels. Why do you think this is so? Write down three main reasons.

a ....

b ....

c ....

National Curriculum links

- Physical processes
- Energy resources and energy transfer

If you can describe some alternative energy resources and explain their uses you are working at level 6.

Links with the Classbook

Unit 110
pages 230–231

28 Energy as a priority

You are going to take part in some unusual group work. If you follow the instructions, you will make a list of ways of saving energy without having to take part in long discussions. This method is used in business to reach quick agreement. It is called **Nominal Group Technique**.

What to do

1 **Individually**, write down five ways that people could save energy.

a .... **d** ....

b .... **e** ....

c ....

2 Take it in turns to read out your list. Write down all the ideas on one piece of paper.

3 Now vote! Do this by each giving five points to the idea you think is best and so on down to one point for your fifth favourite.

4 Read out your votes in turn and work out the total score for each idea.

5 Make a group list of priorities by completing the table.

Our group list

1	....	☐ pts
2	....	☐ pts
3	....	☐ pts
4	....	☐ pts
5	....	☐ pts

National Curriculum links

■ Physical processes ■ Energy resources and energy transfer

If you can describe many examples of energy resources and how they might be conserved you would be working at level 6.

Links with the Classbook

Unit 114
pages 238–239